WE ARE POETS!

In 2004 Helên Thomas joined forces with primary school teacher Kate McGann and devised the performance piece *We Are Poets!*

In the roles of Penelope Page and Gabby Mouth, they ask the all-important questions: What is a poet? What does a poet do? What do poets look like? Performances are followed by workshops that enable children to write and perform their own work with confidence.

All of the poems in this book were written by Helên and feature in the original *We Are Poets!* show or in the follow up *We Are Poets Stuck In The Airport!*

For more information about performances and workshops please visit: www.creativewomensnetwork.co.uk/CWNWeArePoets.htm.

First published in 2008 by
Mucusart Publications
6 Chiffon Way, Trinity Riverside, Gtr Manchester M3 6AB
www.mucusart.co.uk/press.htm

Printed in Great Britain by
www.booksondemand-worldwide.com

ISBN 978 0 9555092 0 9

WE ARE POETS!
Helên Thomas

illustrated by Paul Neads

mucusart publications

For my nephew Thomas Walker
and my good friends Frankie and Ce Ce McGann

Contents:

SCABBY KNEES

Scabby knees! Scabby knees!
Can I pick them; can I please?
They're so itchy, brown and scratchy,
Crusty, flaky and quite nasty,
Like burnt pastry on a pasty,
If I pick them Mum might catch me.

Scabby knees! Scabby knees!
Can I pick them; can I please?
Can I scratch them; can I pick them?
Can I pull bits off and flick them?

Scabby knees! Scabby knees!
I got them falling from the trees,
Onto hard ground with a thud,
Playing games of Robin Hood,
My knees would be scab free they would,
If I had fallen in the mud!

Scabby knees! Scabby knees!
Can I pick them; can I please?
Can I scratch them; can I pick them?
Can I pull bits off and flick them?

Scabby knees! Scabby knees!
Look like they've got a bad disease,
Crispy coated with dried blood,

Underneath there's gunky crud,
I would ban them if I could,
Scabby knees are just no good!

IN THE TOYSHOP

In the toyshop, they've got stocks
Of wooden bricks and building blocks;
Magic tricks in a lockable box,
And if you're ill with chicken pox,
They've colouring books and dot to dot.
There's a dolly with a brolly, a buggy and a cot,
Nappies, shopping trolleys, and ever such a lot
Of socks and frilly frocks, and a tiny wee pot.

In the toyshop they've got trucks
That you can push, plus pull along ducks,
Tractors, trailers, a hen that clucks.
They've pots and pans for tiny cooks,
To bake toy cakes and make believe lunch.
There's a theatre full of puppets; they're a real ugly bunch,
They squabble over sausages with Judy and Punch,
And an evil alligator whose teeth go 'crunch!'

In the toyshop they've got stacks
Of clockwork trains that run on tracks,
Big bags of marbles; sacks of jacks;
'Top Trumps'; 'Old Maid'; 'Snap' cards in packs.
To paint, there's a model jumbo jet,
To win a Nobel medal, there's a Chemistry set,
Don't get into a muddle with a virtual pet,
Buy a doll to molly coddle that cries when wet.

In the toyshop they've got heaps
Of action men in dark green jeeps;
A load of toads; a frog that leaps
And light up robots that make 'beeps'.
You can stage fights with dragons and knights,
There's fancy dress for Halloween with vampire bats that bite,
Spooky masks and wizard hats; fake blood to cause a fright,
Or if the wind is right, you might *just* buy a kite.

In the toyshop they've got lots
Of pirate ships and sailing yachts;
Pads and pens for doodles and jots
With bits and bobs and you-know-whats.
Dress up as a clown, and paint your face.
Ride a hobby-donkey, or a horse, and win a race.
If they closed the toyshop, it would be a disgrace!
I love the toyshop; it is my favourite place.

There once was an old man from Wales,
Who often ate slugs and some snails,
He'd chomp on raw fish,
But his favourite dish,
Was pig's feet with boiled entrails!

MY BABY BROTHER

My baby brother looks like a pig,
He's got less hair than Grandad; he should wear a wig.

My baby brother always smells of poo,
He has to wear a nappy; he doesn't use the loo!

My baby brother cannot walk or talk,
He's such a messy eater; he can't use a knife or fork!

My baby brother really is a bore,
All he does is gurgle and roll round on the floor.

My baby brother is grumpy, spoilt and fat,
He isn't fun to play with; he really is a brat.

My baby brother is just no use to me,
He cannot ride a bicycle; he cannot climb a tree.

My baby brother is too young to run and jump,
So why is he so tired? I think he's a lazy lump.

My baby brother sleeps for hours on end,
He can't sit up or throw a ball; he's no good as a friend.

My baby brother snoozes soundly as a log,
I think that we should sell him, so I can have a dog!

EVERYBODY EVERYWHERE STOMP YOUR FEET!

Everybody everywhere stomp your feet,
Wave your hands in the air if you like sweets,
Flap your wings like a bird that goes "Tweet, tweet",
Everybody everywhere stomp your feet!

Everybody everywhere bang a drum,
Everybody everywhere chew some gum,
Everybody everywhere wave to Mum,
Everybody everywhere rub your tum.

Everybody everywhere stomp your feet,
Wave your hands in the air if you like sweets,
Flap your wings like a bird that goes "Tweet, tweet",
Everybody everywhere stomp your feet!

Everybody everywhere make your arms fold,
Everybody everywhere pretend you're cold,
Everybody everywhere be big and bold,
Everybody everywhere, do as you're told.

Everybody everywhere stomp your feet,
Wave your hands in the air if you like sweets,
Flap your wings like a bird that goes "Tweet, tweet",
Everybody everywhere stomp your feet!

Everybody everywhere make eyebrows,
Every body everywhere show me how,

Everybody everywhere moo like a cow,
Everybody everywhere take a bow.

Everybody everywhere stomp your feet,
Wave your hands in the air if you like sweets,
Flap your wings like a bird that goes "Tweet, tweet",
Everybody everywhere stomp your feet!

I WENT ON A TRIP AND THEN I CAME BACK, AND HERE IS A LIST OF WHAT I PACKED...

An assortment of anoraks and ankle socks,
Bright bouncing beach balls blue,
Castanets, a camera, chopsticks and a clock,
Don't forget the didgeridoo,
Essential equipment for all expeditions,
Flip-flops and a Frisbee,
Gloves and a guidebook that's the latest edition,
Hula-hoops and a hanky,
Important information, ink-pens and ice packs,
Jumpers, jeans, pyjamas,
Kites, ketchup, kaftans, knickers, kickers and knick-knacks,
Luggage labels and leg warmers,
Marmite, make-up, mobile phone, magazines and maps,
Nailbrush, nightie, nachos,
Open-toed sandals, ouzo, oven-gloves and macs,
Pantaloons, back-backs and ponchos,
Quick acting, queasy quelling, travel sickness pills,
Roller-blades and loo rolls,
Slippy, slimy, sloppy sunscreen that very often spills,
Toothbrush and trainers with insoles,
Underpants, umbrellas and umpteen other things,
Verruca cream and vests,
Wellies, woollies, waders, waistcoats and water wings,
Xylophones and X-ray specs,
Yellow Pages, yoga mats, yams and a yashmak,
Zebra patterned swimsuit that's stripy white and black,

I went on a trip and then I came back
And all of it fitted into my rucksack!

BURPING BERYL

Here's a tale about a big fat lass,
Called Burping Beryl; she was full of gas.
Beryl was a great big burping lump,
And when she wasn't burping, Beryl would trump!
She'd belch all day whilst watching telly,
Letting out burps, loud and smelly.
One day she ate a great big cake,
And belched so much, the earth did quake.
Beryl's house was turned to rubble,
"Oh dear," she said, "Now I'm in trouble!"
Beryl felt like such a twerp,
She'd blasted out a great big burp
That made a supersonic sound,
And knocked her house right to the ground.
So, Beryl and her husband Ted
Had to move into the shed,
Where there wasn't very much room,
But it wasn't long before a 'BOOM!'
Could be heard from Beryl's garden,
Ted said, "Beryl! I beg your pardon!"
Burping Beryl was filled with dread,
She'd burped again and wrecked the shed,
Reducing it to firewood,
Ted said, "Beryl, this is no good!"
The shed was in bits on the floor,
Because of Beryl's perilous roar.
"We've got nowhere to live now!" shouted Ted,

"We haven't got a house and we haven't got a bed!"
Then all of a sudden Beryl pointed to the sky,
A hot air balloon was floating by,
"Eureka!" she cried, "Hurrah! I've cracked it!
We'll buy one of those and live in the basket.
I've blown up our house, now I'll blow up a balloon,
I'll fill it full of burp gas and fly us to the moon."
So Beryl bought a big balloon and filled it with a burp,
She took Ted off on holiday to Frankfurt and Antwerp,
And now they live quite safely, happy in the sky,
In Burping Beryl's belch fuelled balloon, forever flying high!

There once was a girl from year three,
Who decided to live in a tree,
Which may seem absurd,
But she looked like a bird,
And often ate worms for her tea!

WHY FRUIT BATS MUST ALWAYS EAT FRUIT

Fred fruit bat was overweight,
Because of all the food he ate,
For dinner he was never late,
He couldn't wait to fill his plate,

With chicken nuggets and beetroot;
Egg fried rice; Chinese bean shoots;
Biscuits made with arrowroot,
But Fred fruit bat would not eat fruit.

He'd eat hot pot, with cheese and beans,
Fish and chips and cold sardines.
Sometimes, he *would* eat his greens,
But Fred would not eat tangerines.

Fred would feast on fried iguanas,
Fish cakes made with live piranhas,
Plain scones baked without sultanas,
But Fred would not eat bananas.

He'd eat cakes and leave no crumbs,
But Fred would never eat fruit gums,
Apricots or purple plums;
He would give them to his chums.

Though he'd refuse all blue berries,
Nectarines and dark black cherries,

Fred once ate a toad called Terry,
After drinking wine and sherry.

Then one day fat Fred fell ill,
He said, "Of food I've had my fill;
Perhaps I'm suffering from a chill,
Fetch the doctor and a pill!"

So, Fred saw a fine physician,
Who said, "This is my suspicion,
I think you've got malnutrition,
You must see a dietician!

You're not eating properly!"
Fred said, "No, that cannot be,
I eat breakfast, lunch and tea,
With second helpings, sometimes three."

"No, that's wrong," the doctor said,
"You're eating too much stodge and bread;
A fruit bat must eat fruit instead,
Or end up staying ill in bed."

So, Fred tried out the doctor's plan,
Eating peaches from a can,
Apples, grapes and lemon flan,
And something called a rambutan.

Fred fruit bat had no excuse,
He had to eat fresh fruit produce:

Gooseberries and orange juice,
Greengages and strawberry mousse.

But all that fruit soon did the trick,
Fred's waistline became thin, not thick,
Because fruit bats should always stick
To fruit, and then, they won't get sick.

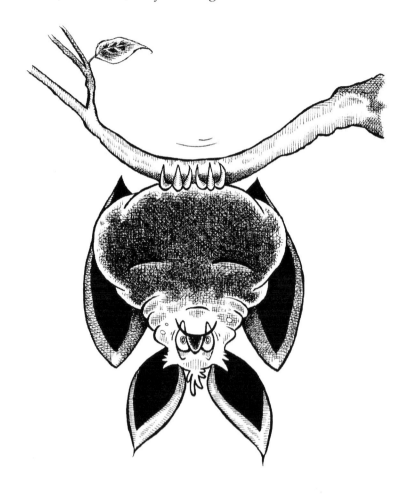

There was a foul boy from year four,
Who had tantrums and rolled on the floor,
Although he was whiny,
He kept the floor shiny,
But stopped when his bottom got sore!

DIRT MAGNET

What's the point of earwax,
And the slime that's up my nose?
Why can't I plant a seed in there,
And see if something grows?

Why is my belly button
Full of fluff and goo?
Why do spilt spaghetti hoops
Stick to me like glue?

Why is there always custard
Dried upon my chin?
And why do I make so much gas
That's better out than in?

Why is there always soil
And grass stains on my knees?
Why do my socks get scuffed with oil
And always smell like cheese?

Why is half the garden
Underneath my nails?
And why does my hair tangle
Like a mesh of mad rats' tails?

Why is that place behind my ears
Always thick with grime.

And why is my grey, unwashed neck
Worse than any crime?

Where does all that dust come from
That's in between my toes,
And why is there so much of it?
My Mum says that she knows

The reason I'm so grungy,
It's a power I exert,
The muck's attracted to me,
I'm a magnet for the dirt!

A teacher who taught in year five,
Liked to eat maggots alive,
She'd pick them up quick,
With a pair of chopsticks,
But never used spoons, forks or knives!

WHERE DO YOU GET YOUR IDEAS?

Where do you get your ideas?
Do they grow in between your big ears?
Do they swim in the streams
Of your nightmares and dreams?
Oh where do you get your ideas?

Where do you get your ideas?
Do they come when you drink special beers?
Do you take magic potions
That stir your emotions?
Oh where do you get your ideas?

Oh where do you get your ideas?
Do you visit witch doctors and seers?
Do you chat with wise wizards,
Magicians and lizards,
Oh where do you get your ideas?

Oh where do you get your ideas?
Do you write about laughter and tears?
Do you fill up your pad
When you're glad, sad, or mad?
Oh where do you get your ideas?

Where do I get my ideas?
I write about things that I hear.
I look all around,

I describe shapes and sounds.
I sniff things as well
And ask: *How does that smell?*
Is it fragrant or sweet?
Would it taste good to eat?
I like to play games,
I ask people their names.
I think: *How do I feel?*
I wonder what's real?
I doodle and write,
I sleep soundly at night
Because if I'm tired
I don't feel inspired.
I travel to places,
See new people's faces.
Sometimes, I sit still,
I get well if I'm ill,
I listen to drums
And the bees as they hum,
I investigate ants,
I love animals and plants,
I make notes as I'm walking
And when people are talking,
I let my mind wander
To daydream and ponder.
I read books and watch plays,
These are just a few ways
To set brains in motion
With poetic notions.
Ideas can't be forced,

They take time, like good sauce,
But they come in due course.
Now please, can you tell me,
Where do you get yours?

ANY-TOWN* SCHOOL SUPERSTARS' RAP

[Insert the name of your school and get your friends to join in!]*

At Any-town we're really top,
We can rhyme, rap and hip-hop!
We are cool dudes and we love words,
We're Any-town superstars, not nerds,
We're here to share some poetry,
At Any-town school join in with me!

Chorus:
Any-town school,
Any-town school is cool
Any-town school
If you don't go to Any-town you're a fool!
Any-town school
We're Any-town school, and we rule
Any-town school
We're superstars at Any-town school
Any-town school.

We're top at sport and games and gym,
We love to run and jump and swim.
We're well behaved and really brainy,
We don't play outside when it's rainy.
If teacher says 'shhhh' we make no sound,
We're the most obedient school around,
At...

Any-town school
Any-town school is cool
Any-town school
If you don't go to Any-town you're a fool!
Any-town school
We're Any-town school and we rule
Any-town school
We're superstars at Any-town school
Any-town school

At Any-town school we're the best,
We take exams and pass maths tests.
At Any-town school we're so bright,
We learn to count and read and write.
Lessons are well taught and well planned,
Our school's the greatest in the land!

Any-town school
Any-town school is cool
Any-town school
If you don't go to Any-town you're a fool!
Any-town school
We're Any-town school and we rule
Any-town school
We're superstars at Any-town school
Any-town school
Yay!

A year six girl with very long hair,
Either did not know or did not care,
That her hair contained nits,
And a nest of blue tits,
An owl and three grizzly bears!

I HATE TESTS!

I hate tests!
Though I always do my best,
I'd rather wash my vest,
Than sit and take a test.
I hate tests!

I hate tests!
And I would like to suggest,
That setting people tests,
Makes them feel stressed.
I hate tests!

I hate tests!
Tests make me depressed,
I'm tired and want a rest,
I'll take a trip to Budapest.
I hate tests!

I hate tests!
Tests are pests,
Like rats in nests,
Or unwanted guests.
I hate tests!

I hate tests!
Yes, tests I detest,
I shall make it my life's quest,

To protest against tests.
I hate tests!

I hate tests!
Now, I've expressed
My opinion of tests;
I've got it off my chest.
I hate tests!
Do you hate tests?
Well I hate tests!

There was a professor from Spain,
Who said, "I have got a big brain!"
Although he was bright,
He had poor eyesight,
And got hit by a fast, passing train!

VANILLA VILLANELLE

For afters I will always eat ice cream,
It is my all time favourite dessert,
I'd eat it 'til I burst at every seam.

Ice cream is super cool and so supreme,
With other puddings I would never flirt,
For afters I will always eat ice cream,

Sometimes, it's so cold that it makes me scream,
I scoff it though my teeth and molars hurt,
I'd eat it 'til I burst at every seam.

Eating ice cream makes me smile and beam,
I care not if I get fat and split my skirt,
For afters I will always eat ice cream,

Ice cream excites me, it makes my eyes gleam,
My tongue and taste buds switch to high alert,
I'd eat it 'til I burst at every seam.

In my dreams I'm in an ice cream eating team,
I sport a Neapolitan striped shirt,
For afters I will always eat ice cream,
I'd eat it 'til I burst at every seam.

WHY YOU WON'T SEE ME TRAVELLING BY BUS!

I was travelling by bus one day to a far off town,
When the bus began to judder and the driver formed a frown,
The road was very bumpy; all the people bounced around,
The engine started spluttering; I thought it would break down,
But the driver of the jumpy bus sped on and drove so quick,
I had to shout out, "Stop the bus, I think I might be sick!"

But still the driver drove on; he seemed in such a hurry,
I heard my tummy gurgle and I began to worry,
Because I'd had a greedy lunch of eggs, chips, peas and curry,
Followed by an apple pie, milkshake and McFlurry,
My slurpy belly sloshed and churned like an oil slick,
So I shouted, "Stop the bus, I think I might be sick!"

But the driver wasn't listening to my plaintive cry,
And though it was a summer's day, with air so hot and dry,
The windows of the bus were shut; I thought we all would fry,
My stomach ached and burbled, I felt like I would die,
The pain inside my tummy felt like a donkey's kick,
So I shouted, "Stop the bus, I think I might be sick!"

I yelled, "Please, PLEASE stop the bus!" this time I was sure,
I tried to run, fast as I could, down towards the door,
But, too late, I heaved and retched my guts up on the floor,
And before I could apologise, I hurled up even more.
Out it surged in bucket loads, warm and brown and thick,
So I shouted, "Stop the bus because I've just been sick!"

Then a third and final spray of lumpy sick came out,
It covered everything and everyone round and about,
In chunky, gunky, gloopy sludge that smelt like sauerkraut,
But the driver carried on because *he* hadn't heard my shouts.
So, when we stopped and he turned off his i-pod with a 'click!'
I pointed to the vomit and said, "I think *someone's* been sick!"

And that's why you won't see me travelling by bus!

There once was a boy from New York,
Who was an embarrassing dork,
He was clumsy and nerdy,
And walked most absurdly,
With long skinny legs like a stork!

QUEASY CALYPSO

If your tummy's feeling funny,
And you're running to the loo,
Here's a list of things you just shouldn't do:

Don't jump around on a pogo stick,
Because if you do you're gonna be sick.
If you're green around the gills and feeling grim,
It's not a good idea to go to the gym.

If your tummy's feeling funny,
And you're running to the loo,
Here's a list of things you just shouldn't do:

If you've got a fuzzy tongue and a fizzy dizzy feeling,
Do not go trampolining.
If you've got gut rot from eating unripe mangoes,
Don't attempt to fox trot or try to tango!

If your tummy's feeling funny,
And you're running to the loo,
Here's a list of things you just shouldn't do:

If your belly's aching and your head is thumping,
Do not go bungee jumping.
If you've been sitting on the toilet for hours and hours,
Don't decide to try the rides at Alton Towers!

If your tummy's feeling funny,
And you're running to the loo,
Here's a list of things you just shouldn't do:

If you're feeling ill at ease and you've got a constant sneeze,
Don't join the circus and learn the trapeze.
Here's my advice to you, what you should do instead,
Take the day off school and stay in bed!

If your tummy's feeling funny,
And you're running to the loo,
That was a list of things you just shouldn't do!

SOME INTERESTING FACTS ABOUT DANGEROUS CREATURES

Tarantulas inject venom through their large fangs,
They don't live in colonies or in big gangs,
They live in silk lined burrows and have been known,
To eat each other – they prefer life alone,
Though lack of food is not something they fear,
The females can live on just water for years,
They have hairs that sting, which might itch, but not kill you,
Unlike the bite of the malarial mosquito…

Although there are creatures and beasts that are scarier,
In Africa mosquito bites spread malaria.
The female mosquito requires blood to make
Her eggs, and the blood is like a protein shake.
As she drinks the blood, she transmits a disease
That kills millions of people, it's hard to believe
That such a small insect can be so deadly,
Compared to her, crocodiles seem safe and friendly…

Although they have got sharp, spiky smiles,
You cannot trust Nile crocodiles.
They've lived on the earth for millions of years,
It's said that when crocs eat, they weep salty tears,
They snooze open mouthed and the birds gather round,
Picking insects and food from teeth stained blood brown,
Crocodiles eat almost anything they're so unscrupulous,
Feasting freely on fish or a fat hippopotamus…

Though crocodiles kill, many people have died,
Attacked by the hippo whose mouth is quite wide.
In Africa hippos dislike meeting strangers,
If you disturb hippos you'll be in grave danger,
The hippo will happily kill you with zeal,
But he will not eat you for his midday meal,
He's vegetarian; meat's not part of his culture,
So, he'll kill you and leave you as food for the vulture…

Vultures are birds and they live where it's hot,
So to cool down, you'll never guess what
The turkey vulture chooses to do -
He cools down his legs with his own poo!
Vultures eat animals that are dead or dying,
Detecting the smell whilst in the sky flying,
And if you don't fancy finding your food like that,
Wait 'til I tell you about the vampire bat…

The only known animals to live solely on blood,
Vampire bats' eyesight must be very good,
Because they're nocturnal - they come out at night,
So you will not see them in bright, broad daylight.
Every night each bat must drink half its own weight,
Sometimes the well-fed bats regurgitate
Blood, which they share with their sisters and brothers,
Though they're scary to us, bats are kind to each other!

LET'S GLOBE TROT!

Let's globe trot, I'll tell you what,
Oh, let's go round the world,
Take the plane, come home again,
Fly sky high like a bird,
Hurry up, no time to stop,
Let's see what we can see,
On the hop, this trip's tip top,
Come take a tour with me!

Stamp your feet to a Samba beat,
Play football in Brazil,
Don't misbehave, do a Mexican wave,
Come with me if you will,
To where it's hot, on a sailing yacht
Or on a huge cruise liner,
Roller skate off to Kuwait,
Ride a motorbike to China!

Let's globe trot, I'll tell you what,
Oh, let's go round the world,
Take the plane, come home again,
Fly sky high like a bird,
Hurry up, no time to stop,
Let's see what we can see,
On the hop, this trip's tip top,
Come take a tour with me!

Surfboard balance on a wave,
Take the train to Crewe,
Jog down to Johannesburg,
Trek round Kathmandu,
Drive a car, near and far,
Paddle a canoe,
Fly a rocket to the stars,
Just to see the view!

Let's globe trot, I'll tell you what,
Oh, let's go round the world,
Take the plane, come home again,
Fly sky high like a bird,
Hurry up, no time to stop,
Let's see what we can see,
On the hop, this trip's tip top,
Come take a tour with me!

WHEN ALL THE WORLD WAS MADE OF SUGAR

Long, long ago,
Before the time we call 'primordial'
The world was made of sugar,
And the sea was lime cordial.
The fish were made of jelly,
But they didn't have a sting,
They were sweet and filled your belly,
With a wobble and a zing.
All the waterfalls were flowing,
With cool fizzy orangeade:
Carrot coloured soda pop,
Dropping a cascade,
Of sparkly, skipping, bubbles,
Spilling down into a lake
Of sherbet, where the lily pads
Were made of Jaffa Cakes,
Floating on the surface,
Feeding families of frogs,
Watched by friendly crocodiles
Eating chocolate logs.

There was a young boy from Brazil,
Who loved to play football until,
The cup final game,
The boy became lame,
And lost the cup final ten nil!

MEMORY BEACH

At weekends, on holidays, in all sorts of weather,
With swimsuits and wellies we go to the beach,
With buckets of upside-down sand we build castles,
And dig moats around them that fill up with sea.

We gather dry starfish as brittle as biscuits,
Driftwood sandpapered and washed by the waves;
Pebbles, glass smooth, shaped by years in the ocean,
We sift through the flotsam for shells in shy coves.

We ponder the rock pools and wonder of mermaids,
Tell tall tales of jellyfish stings and jump clear,
Dare to touch seaweed and dead crabs, so stinky,
Jabbing and jousting a snapped craggy claw.

As pirates swashbuckling, we plunder dune islands,
Tumbling down gullies of hot windblown sand.
Playing cool cowboys and super Sioux Indians,
We slay mutant monsters until the day's end.

Back by the bay, the tide's turning, waves breaking,
Invading the shoreline, the swell of the sea
Floods moats; our fortress defences fall crumbling,
Collapsing sandcastles that sweep clean away.

ROCK-POP WORM AND THE BIG BUG BAND

Sit down, have a biscuit and a glass of milk,
And I'll tell you a tale about some worms who weave silk.
They make shiny socks for feet, and glossy gloves for hands,
But when they have the day off, they're in a rock band.
The lead singer is called Rock-Pop, and he's the top worm,
He's got a stripy body stocking and a curly perm,
He strums a small guitar, and plays on 'Top of the Pops',
Backed by The Big Bug Band, Rock-Pop Worm bops until he drops.

Oh Rock-Pop Worm and The Big Bug Band,
The best gang of rock star, pop worms in the land,
By day they sell silk socks in The Big Bug Pop Sock Shop,
Then disco dance all night, the music never stops.

The Big Bugs know a rival band called The Revolving Rocks,
A revolting group of grungy grubs, who never wash their socks,
Their front man is Mick Maggot; he likes to sing and prance,
But Big Bug Band and Rock-Pop think he's a load of pants.
Both bands got invited to a party in the park,
It was called 'Woodwormstock', it started after dark,
Mick Maggot said to Rock-Pop, "We'll put you to the test!
Let's see who plays the longest, the loudest and the best."

Oh Rock-Pop Worm and The Big Bug Band,
The best gang of rock star, pop worms in the land,
By day they sell silk socks in The Big Bug Pop Sock Shop,
Then disco dance all night, the music never stops.

And so there did ensue an all night battle of the bands,
The Big Bug Band and Rock-Pop played to a field of frenzied fans,
Whilst over on a different stage, Mick Maggot and his mates,
Were making mucky music, and shouting, "Aren't we great?"
Both bands played through the night until the following Sunday,
When the owner of the park said it was time to go away.
As the crowd began to shout out for one band to be the winner,
A flock of hungry starlings landed, looking for some dinner.

Oh Rock-Pop Worm and The Big Bug Band,
The best gang of rock star, pop worms in the land,
By day they sell silk socks in The Big Bug Pop Sock Shop,
Then disco dance all night, the music never stops.

As Mick Maggot and his cronies had performed their final song,
The birds had heard the noise, then recognised the grubby pong,
A passing song thrush shouted, "Oh they're such a rowdy bunch,
I do not like their music, but I'd eat them for my lunch!"
And so the birds descended and devoured Mick and The Rocks,
Because all birds love eating maggots who've got smelly socks,
But they will not touch silk worms who wear clean socks and vests,
That's why The Big Bug Band survived and Rock-Pop's still the best!

Oh Rock-Pop Worm and The Big Bug Band,
The best gang of rock star, pop worms in the land,
By day they sell silk socks in the Big Bug Pop Sock Shop,
Then disco dance all night, the music never stops.

Oh Rock-Pop Worm and The Big Bug Band,
The best gang of rock star pop worms in the land!

Helên Thomas is a performance poet who appears regularly on the UK poetry circuit.

Her first taste of poetic success came in 1985 when she won a prize in *She* Magazine's National Poetry Competition with "Ode To Bad Poetry". In October 2000 she won the Manchester Poetry Festival Slam. Her poems have appeared in various magazines and anthologies in print and online.

She has performed at a range of venues including schools, libraries, tents, a canal barge, an ancient historical monument, lots of pubs and the occasional theatre. She has wowed audiences from Borders Books to The Bowery Club New York; from folk clubs to fringe festivals; from Cheshire to Cheltenham, and she once won a karaoke competition in Cairns, Australia!

To order more copies of *We Are Poets!* or for other titles from Mucusart Publications, please visit www.mucusart.co.uk/press.htm.